Self-Care for the Caregiver

*A guilt-free way to love
yourself while caring
for others*

MAYDIS SKEETE

ISBN: 978-1-0880-3961-8

Table of Contents

DEDICATION

I dedicate this book to my mother, Norma R. Caldwell, who taught me so much about life.

She modeled what caregiving is and allowed me the honor of caring for her.

ACKNOWLEDGMENTS

I thank my special friends, Alvin and Deborah Davis, my college biology classmate, Dr. Enacio Hunt, and my dear husband, Randy Skeete, for reading each chapter carefully to proofread the manuscript.

I thank my accountability buddy, Afina Taua, who was a great support and encourager throughout the process.

I thank R.A.A. Chamara for designing the book cover and working patiently with me through many drafts.

FOREWORD

Do you ever feel like you are on the edge of a breakdown or find yourself stressed about work, home, and social life while being a diligent caregiver? *Self-Care for the Caregiver: A guilt-free way to love yourself while caring for others* provides the antidote to such a dilemma.

The author, Maydis Skeete, addresses this concern with passion and experience as she strives to help caregivers navigate the maze of how to include self-care with the busy role of caregiving. Providing carefully reviewed explanations and guidance, she unfolds chapter by chapter the necessary criteria and the challenges to step away from to conquer this crisis. Researched principles that have been successful in providing mental, physical, and spiritual benefits are applied here and wrapped as a gift to caregivers to help them win over any personal struggles with self-care.

This book encourages one to practice self-awareness and focus on the present instead of meaningless racing day after day from one task to the next. The recommended 7-step program provides gifts of self-love everyone should adopt. This is a must-read for everyone wanting to experience more balance and self-care in their life and especially an adult caregiver. This book is an informative and practical guide, with every chapter inspiring you to a wellness revelation.

Robert G. Allen
5x New York Times Best Selling Author

ABOUT THE AUTHOR

Maydis Caldwell Skeete is a lifelong learner, a passionate administrator, and a champion of God-given health principals. She holds a Bachelor of Science in Biology/Medical Technology and Master of Public Administration /Health Care Administration. Mrs. Skeete is a member of the Society of Human Resource Management, American Heart Association, American College of Sports Medicine, and the Functional Aging Institute. Mrs. Skeete is the owner and president of 'Get Up and Mooove, LLC: personal training that's fun and effective'. Her services are specialized for adults over 50+ to promote joint/bone health, strength, balance, and mobility.

Her recent publication "Self-Care for the Caregiver" provides insight and practical information that will guide a reader to greater self-awareness and wellness concepts. The knowledge gathered from a 40-year career at the renowned Michigan Medicine Health System, an understanding of Biblical principles and the personal life experiences of Mrs. Skeete and others engaged in caregiving, make this publication a reality.

Mrs. Skeete retired from Health Care Administration in 2019 and now serves as a wellness coach and personal trainer in Ann Arbor, Michigan.

INTRODUCTION

If the title of this book interests you, then it is probably safe to say you are a caregiver or know someone you care about who is serving in this role. To be responsible for another person's physical, mental, and often financial well-being is challenging work. It can leave you exhausted at the end of the day and can result in compromise to personal, physical, and mental health.

This book is primarily written for those who are serving as caregivers for a family member in the home. However, each of the steps presented is useful for anyone who has too much to do and too little time.

The simple steps outlined are not new to most of us. They may not remove all the challenges one may face as a caregiver. There still may be days that seem completely crazy, and times you want to walk away and scream. However, with a commitment to the process, you will experience more control and calmness. You will develop a healthier lifestyle and overall feel better about yourself and the work you do.

The intent of this book is to provide a process that will reinforce your wellness knowledge and give a gift of self-love with each chapter to help keep you focused on the importance of self-care. A separate book, "The Real Life Self-Care Journal," is also available and recommended to assist in tracking progress on the self-care journey.

MY STORY

I spent over six years caring for my elderly mother after she suffered a debilitating fall that left her paralyzed and unable to walk. She remained in her home but was located an hour away from my home. My siblings were located more than 10 hours away in other states and were not able to provide regular on-site assistance. I had to find other help to spend the night and help with daily hygiene as she needed 24-hour care. I would stay with her during the weekends, and if I had no one to cover some weekdays, I would rearrange my schedule so I could handle that also.

Every Friday evening after working a full day, I made a pilgrimage to my mother's home to indulge in cooking, shopping, reviewing the mail, paying the bills, and spending important time with her. I took care of the set-up of medications to be dispensed daily (I didn't trust anyone else to handle this) and made sure she had transportation to go to the doctor on the right day at the right time. When things broke down in the home, I contacted someone to get things fixed.

On Sunday evenings, I would return to my home to get ready for work at the medical center where I was employed.

I took pride in my career in health administration, my active church offices, meeting my sale targets that kept my home business thriving, and being a dutiful caregiver. "Life is busy, but I got this," so I thought.

For several years, I lived this routine every week. On many days I did not feel up to the task, but I did it anyway. Soon, I found myself often tired and irritable. I wasn't getting adequate sleep, and weight gain was beginning to creep up. I convinced myself that these were nothing to be too concerned about. I just needed to go to bed earlier and cut down on the sweets. I enjoyed cookies and cake and always had something in the pantry at my home and my mother's home to satisfy the sweet cravings.

Upon arrival to work one morning, I made a call to my physician. I thought I probably should schedule an appointment for a check-up. I had experienced sharp chest pain while jogging on the treadmill the prior evening. I thought it probably was nothing too much to worry about because it lasted only a moment and subsided when I lowered the speed. I felt okay and was able to complete my workout. But this was the second time a sharp chest pain had occurred and then quickly subsided. The first being 3 weeks prior while I was running across the street at a stoplight.

That call to my physician resulted in a trip to the Emergency Room (ER), where several tests and blood analysis warranted admittance for a cardiac catheterization. A 90% blockage was discovered in the main artery. I was on the brink of a serious illness or death if this had resulted in a massive heart attack.

I asked myself, "How could this happen? I don't drink alcohol, smoke, or eat meat. My cholesterol has always been well within the normal range, and I exercise." What could have gone wrong? I could not believe it!

While convalescing, I spent a lot of time in prayer and thinking about this close call on my life. I prayerfully pondered and reviewed the daily routines I had faithfully practiced at work, home, church, and the various activities to which I had committed for so many years. Careful examination of my commitments, diet, and stress level came into focus. I had to acknowledge that I had stretched myself too thin with commitments, wasn't consistent with meals or always eating healthy foods, and, most of all, had allowed unhealthy, stressful situations to dominate my life more than necessary. It was time to re-evaluate and reset priorities. This was my "Wake Up Call."

The reason I write this book is to share with others who may be doing a lot for others but not making time to include personal self-care. And I write these words for those who have knowledge of these health principles but don't apply them faithfully.

3

My hope is that you will join me in adopting the 7 steps that provide a gift of self-love and experience a calmer presence, healthier body, and more joy in life.

CHAPTER 1

"Help! I've Fallen and Can't Get Up!"

Most of us have seen a commercial or an advertisement where a person has fallen and is pleading for "HELP!." The sentiments of that commercial are real in the daily life of many caregivers. Every situation is different but let's face it, many people in the caregiving role neglect important personal health principles and care for themselves. Continuing in this manner, month after month and year after year, only results in a tired, irritated, ineffective zombie. Being physically and mentally drained all the time sets the stage for some major diseases that no one wants. The bottom line, caregivers need help.

Step #1: Ask for Help

Yes, it is okay to ask for help. If you are caring for an adult who is suffering a mental or physical debilitation, you will need help. Many caregivers, especially women, will often shoulder the responsibility from week to week without ever taking a day for themselves to recuperate. This is not sustainable.

Others feel they are the only person who can really handle the person's needs and, therefore, must control all aspects of the care. In some cases, the person being cared for wants no one else to attend to them except the caregiver. Each of these scenarios can leave either person exhausted and overly stressed in a way that is detrimental to health if the situation is prolonged.

One of the things I learned from adult caregiving is that you cannot do it alone. You need help, and it is best to put this in place early in the process. You do not want to get to a point where you as a caregiver become sick or debilitated due to ignoring important principles in self-care.

It helps to have a team of reliable people or services available to assist in various situations and for your respite moments. Team members may consist of other family members, close friends, willing church members, neighbors, private agencies, etc.

If you are working another full-time job, especially outside of the home, plus providing caregiving, your life is sure to be constantly busy, and that can be taxing to the brain. Many caregivers in this situation are overwhelmed but feel reluctant or ashamed to ask for help. Some caregivers feel that requesting help is a sign of weakness. Do Not be a victim of that thought process. There are several people who are willing to sit with a person, and also respite care centers and volunteer agencies that support this type of activity. However, one may have to seek out such services.

(The Resource pages at the end of the book list agencies that assist with caregiving).

Research shows that one of the subtle side effects of constant busyness is chronic stress. Chronic stress is bad, and with it comes health issues like hypertension, heart disease, and strokes.[1] A caregiver needs to exhibit some assertiveness and ask family or friends for support as they navigate this role in caregiving. Assertiveness is the antidote to chronic stress.

Regardless of whom you may care for, an elderly parent, spouse, child, or another adult, the caregiving experience is like no other. It is not an easy task. There is much to learn, and depending on the circumstance, you may have to make a quick turn when medications change, an accident happens, an all-night stay at the hospital ER occurs, or one of the helpers gets sick, etc. Caregivers need a team. I would suggest a minimum of 3-4 reliable people who may be called upon or scheduled to assist in times of need and for respite moments.

Go ahead and take that first step in your self-care journey by requesting HELP! You don't want to end up in a place where you are calling for help because you are emotionally or physically in a place where you can't get up.

A wise King Solomon wrote, "Two are better than one because they have a good reward for their labor. For if they fall, one will lift up his companion; but woe to him that is alone when he falls; for he hath no one to help him up." Eccl. 4:9,10.

Your Gift of Self-love: Ask for help

Six Steps to Consider As You Build Your 'Help' Team

1. Reach out to others who have already walked this path. Seek their advice and learn from their experiences. These individuals can often provide you with new resources and guidance to help you on this journey.

2. Contact your local Area Agency on Aging or Well Spouse Association, if applicable to your situation, and ask for guidance.

3. Let family members, close friends, pastor, rabbi, or priest know of your dilemma and request their assistance or recommendations.

4. Hire someone to assist with special tasks or caregiving.

5. Don't turn people away who want to help unless there is a really good reason.

6. Speak with your physician, health care provider, or social worker and request their assistance on available resources.

Notes: Where I Can Find Help

"Pearls don't lie on the seashore, if you want one you must dive for it."
~ Chinese Proverb

CHAPTER 2

Just Say NO!

When a toddler's favorite word is "no," that is often a declaration that the terrible twos' have arrived. According to experts in child development, "no" is a wonderful word for your child to acquire. It is an important milestone for children and often a way for them to celebrate their newly found independence. "No" is the beginning of the child defining him or herself.

What does this have to do with self-care?

Well, something happens between childhood and adulthood. While a toddler is learning to define his/her independence with the word "no," most adults have learned to hate to say "no." Most of us don't want to disappoint or hurt someone, especially our friends or family members, so we are reluctant to tell them "no."

Sometimes we do things that make others feel better or for them to "like us." Even when it's not quite what we want to do, we end up begrudgingly adding another commitment to an already full schedule and later suffer the consequence.

In other cases, some people have a hard time saying "no" because they have several interests and want to explore and be involved in everything.

I admit I have had a challenge with saying "no." After adding caregiving to my schedule, I had to learn to think twice and identify what could reasonably be done, and respectfully turn down those that didn't fit. Saying "no" isn't about turning people down; it is just a clear way to set boundaries.

When we say "yes" to things that aren't a priority, that pushes the important things you want or need to do further down on your list. This brings on feelings of frustration, stress, and being overwhelmed. The important point I am making is to choose wisely outside commitments. An article written by Jonathan Becher was printed in Forbes Business, and it offered several quotes from powerful men who considered "no" to be an important part of a successful life strategy. Here are three examples:

Steve Jobs: "Focusing is about saying no."

Warren Buffet: "We need to learn the slow "yes" and the quick "no."

Tony Blair: "The art of leadership is saying no, not saying yes. It is easy to say yes."[2]

Filling unavailable time with projects, commitments, and other activities that do not interest you or bring a solid benefit to the table is a recipe for unnecessary added stress. Be selective on all outside activities, so a full cup doesn't overflow.

Step #2: Learn To Say "No"

Four questions to ask yourself before accepting projects/commitments:

1. Is this something that I need to do?
2. Is this something I want to do?
3. Am I the only one who can do this?
4. Do I have time to do this?

If you answered "no" to any of those questions, think twice before giving a commitment of "yes."

Your Gift of Self-love:
Guard your time; Exercise your independence, and say "no."

Notes: How I Will Guard My Time

_____

_____

_____

_____

_____

_____

_____

_____

_____

CHAPTER 3

Get More Sleep

Do you often get to midday with a drowsy feeling? If you responded yes, you are not alone. The number of people not getting adequate sleep is on the rise.

The people hit hardest when it comes to sleep deprivation include police, health care workers, those in the transportation field like truck drivers, and of course, the diligent caregiver.

Step #3: Get Adequate Sleep

Surveys show that 40 percent of American adults get less than the nightly minimum of seven hours recommended by the American Academy of Sleep Medicine and the National Sleep Foundation.[3] The National Institute of Health estimates that between 50 - 70 million people do not get enough sleep.

Why is sleep so important?

Sleep provides rest for the body and mind. When we sleep, our bodies repair, our cells rejuvenate, and muscles have the opportunity to grow. Sleep is important for healthy brain function, also. Studies have shown that good sleep affects our learning ability and our problem-solving skills.

On the other hand, lack of sufficient sleep and low-quality sleep has been connected to many problems and sicknesses. Obesity, increased risk of disease, mood disorders, and a lowered immune system response are a few of the common risks associated with sleep problems.

In the United States, inadequate sleep has been linked to more than 1 out of 5 auto accidents due to drowsy driving.[4] This means that approximately 1 million crashes a year could have been prevented if all drivers got enough sleep. As a caregiver, one needs to be sufficiently rested and alert to carry out responsibilities and decision-making associated with safe caregiving.

Sleep is important, and everyone needs it to function at a decent level. When you get adequate rest, you think, look and feel good. So why do we not get more?

A 2018 research poll from the National Sleep Foundation suggests that one big problem is simply that people do not consider sleep a priority. When ranked from a list of selected items and asked which were most important, only 10% of respondents said sleep. This is far less than cited for the other criteria, which  included fitness, nutrition, work, hobbies, and personal interest.[5]

Are we too preoccupied with work, watching movies, playing sports, eating another snack, or tinkering with electronic equipment that we put off going to bed for valuable sleep? According to research studies, the answer to that question is often "Yes." Many sleep-deprived people fall in a category coined "bedtime procrastinator," and I was one of them.

A team of researchers at Utrecht University in Utrecht, Netherlands, studied this phenomenon and reported results in an issue of the Journal of Frontiers of Psychology.[6]

They found that bedtime procrastination is a real problem and is often associated with general old procrastination, which is a problem with self-regulation. However, bedtime procrastination is unique because while people often procrastinate to put off undesirable tasks, sleep is not generally considered undesirable.

It was speculated that it is not so much a matter of not wanting to go to sleep, but procrastinators do not want to stop the other activities they are doing or feel they need to complete something so they can go to sleep. In many cases, they have waited until the last minute to start something or get distracted by something that entices their interest. For caregivers, this may be as simple as washing that last load of clothes that should have been done earlier, staying up to work on a report that is needed for tomorrow's meeting, baking the cookies you promised for your child's piano recital, surfing the net, watching the late-night news or putting together that special potluck dish you should have said "no" to but it was your best friend who asked and on and on and on. I think you get the picture. All of these and more are things that could be robbing precious sleep if they run into intended sleep time.

Stop and think about it!

Are you a bedtime procrastinator?

Do you get sufficient sleep?

Plan adequate time for sleep and journal your success in the "The Real Life Self-care Journal." It will help to keep you on track.

Your Gift of Self-love:
Get 7-8 hours of sleep each night. Don't become overly occupied with projects or distractions that result in insufficient sleep.

Notes: How I Will Get Adequate Sleep

_____

_____

_____

_____

_____

_____

_____

_____

_____

"Sleep is like the golden chain that binds our health and body together."
~ Thomas Dekker

CHAPTER 4

Choose Life-Giving Nutrients

 Many evenings I have worked late or ventured to a network marketing meeting after work to then come home famished. Not wanting to wait and prepare something, one of the first things I found myself doing was opening the pantry or refrigerator to see what was available to gobble down to ward off the hunger. An encounter with cookies, crackers, ice cream, chips, peanut butter and jelly, and sometimes fruit generally did the trick for momentary relief. Does this sound familiar?

We all know that food and water provide the nutrients we need to sustain life. And I am sure everyone reading this page eats and drinks something, or you wouldn't be here. The question for us to examine is what are we eating and drinking?

There are foods that are life-givers, and there are foods that rob us of our best performance. In this chapter, I want to emphasize good nutrition and why it is important for everyone to choose the life-giver, especially when you are dealing with stressful situations at work, at home, or in life in general.

There are six classes of nutrients. Included are carbohydrates, proteins, fats, vitamins, minerals, and water. All of them are important. If you are considered a normal healthy individual, you should be ingesting a balanced supply of nutrients that restore and repair the body daily. The human body is built up from the foods eaten. There is a constant breakdown of tissues in the body, and each organ requires a share of nutrients to rebuild and repair properly. The brain, blood, nerves, and bones all respond to the type of nutrients taken into the body. That is why it is important to choose life-giving foods. The best way to maintain a good nutritional balance is to eat a wide variety of wholesome foods and drink plenty of water.

Another way to make sure you are getting a balance of wholesome foods is to eat the rainbow. In other words, eat fresh fruits and vegetables that have color.

Grains, fruits, nuts, and vegetables was the diet chosen for mankind by the Creator.[7] These are wholesome, life-giving foods. This ancient dietary practice continues to be a proven, healthy, life-sustaining diet today. National Geographic scientists researched people throughout the world to find those who lived the longest and most productive lives. In that finding were those whose diets consisted primarily of fruit, nuts, grains, and vegetables.[8] For those wanting to develop a habit of eating life-giving foods, prepare more fresh fruit, vegetables, nuts, and grains at meals so that you receive the optimal nutrient balance.

I have encountered many people who whine about the time-consuming effort required to prepare healthy meals. Instead, they resolve to pick up fast food items or frozen microwavable dishes to serve as a meal. This is not good for those being cared for or the caregiver. Food that has not been properly prepared or is overly processed only adds additional problems that may be detrimental to health.

Andrew Weil, MD, a practitioner, author, and the director of the Andrew Weil Center for Integrated Medicine at the University of Arizona, posts a daily nutritional and health blog. In his October 27, 2011 writing, he explains the woes of packaged foods that contribute to inflammation. The article states, "Chronic inflammation is influenced by genetics, a sedentary lifestyle, too much stress, and exposure to environmental toxins such as secondhand tobacco smoke. Diet has a huge impact, so much so that I believe that most people in our part of the world go through life in a pro-inflammatory state as a result of what they eat. I'm convinced that the single most important thing you can do to counter chronic inflammation is to stop eating refined, processed, and manufactured foods... most people consume an excess of omega-6 fatty acids, which the body uses to synthesize compounds that promote inflammation. You get a lot of omega-6 fatty acids from snack foods and fast foods."[9]

There you have it! Over-indulging in microwavable packaged meals, processed cheese, cookies, chips, and pastries promote inflammation, and they typically have very little nutritional value. Eating a variety of wholesome food choices regularly should provide the necessary vitamins and minerals needed. Ample serving of fruits, vegetables, and whole grains every day is ideal.

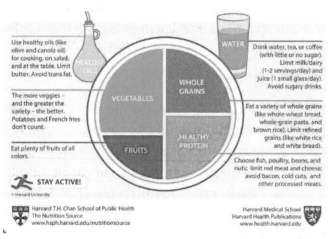

The healthy eating plate created by Harvard School of Public Health researchers provides the healthiest choices of food from the major food groups. See diagram, page 23. The primary premise is that one must eat a variety of fruits and vegetables and select wholesome quality proteins for optimal health. But let's face it, not everyone has access to or knowledge about nutritional needs. We live in a world where people are typically not eating the 5-9 servings of fruits and vegetables recommended.

Our food travels miles before it reaches our tables, and some communities have become "food deserts," lacking access to a variety of fresh food options. It can be a challenge for some people to get the full spectrum of adequate nutrition. In light of these shortcomings regarding our food supply, it may be advantageous to add a nutritional supplement such as a multi-vitamin, to support the system. If you feel you are not getting adequate nutrition, I encourage you to speak with your health care provider or physician.

Supplements should be taken only to promote health and never to excess. The notion that if a little bit is good, then more must be better is not always true. Too much or too little of any one nutrient, specifically in the form of supplements, may increase the risk of poor health. For example, too little Vitamin D could lead to muscle and bone weakness, but too much could be toxic and build up too much calcium in the blood. It is always best to consult your physician to determine which supplements and how much should be taken.

Also, beware of fad diets and misinformation on the television and in magazines. Most of that information has not been critically researched, and it doesn't work for everyone. In some cases, these misguided programs may result in more harm than good. Some people may have food allergies and nutritional complications (e.g. Gluten or lactose intolerance) that make matters worse. Please check with your physician or health care provider for guidance.

It does require effort to prepare and maintain a consistent healthy meal plan, but it is well worth the effort. As a caregiver, organizing your menus and the days to prepare foods will help you stay on target with a regular habit of eating healthy, nutritious foods. On days you prepare meals, cook more than normally needed. Place the extra portions in meal prep containers, label, and freeze so they will be available on days you have less time to cook. Scheduling days to plan and prepare meals helps me to stay focused on eating healthy foods. Also, removing foods like cookies and chips from the pantry makes it easier not to be tempted.

If you work another job, take healthy food and drink (water) with you and make an effort to avoid eating the office snacks. This was a big challenge for me because there was always some sweet treat at the workplace.

Reference the "The Real Life Self-Care Journal" for more tips and guidelines in planning meals and organizing to save time.

In addition to eating at regular times, drinking water throughout the day is extremely important. Water makes up about 60-70 percent of our body weight. Every system in the body depends on this nutrient. Water is a nutrient we cannot live without, yet so many are dehydrated, preferring to drink coffee, tea, and other beverages that cannot take the place of water. Sometimes when one feels hungry, one is really dehydrated and needs to drink water. Even mild dehydration can drain your energy and make you feel tired.

Estimating fluid needs is different for each individual and is typically calculated according to body weight or metabolic weight. How to derive that information for your personal use is outlined in the "The Real Life Self-care Journal." I have learned that drinking 12-16 oz. of water upon rising helps to establish my day and get in my estimated fluid need of 7-8 glasses of water a day.

Step #4: Eat a Variety of Life-Giving Foods and Drink Plenty of Water Daily

"In health and in sickness, pure water is one of heaven's choicest blessings. Its proper use promotes health. It is the beverage that God provided to quench the thirst of animals and people. Drunk freely, it helps to supply the necessities of the system and assists nature to resist disease." The Ministry of Healing, by EG White, page 237

Six Ways to Establish Life-Giving Nutritional Habits

1. Plan your menu each week.
2. When preparing meals cook enough to store extra in meal prep containers to freeze for those days you don't have much time to cook.
3. Establish regular times for meals and try sticking to eating at those times.
4. Carry a water bottle filled with water to remind you to drink more water; add lemon, strawberries, or sliced cucumbers for a refreshing taste.
5. Avoid coffee, tea, alcohol, and sodas; instead, drink water that brings life.
6. Instead of processed foods like cookies and chips, fill your fridge with fruits and healthy snacks.

Your Gift of Self-love: Eat a variety of life-giving foods EVERY DAY; drink water throughout the day. Limit sweets!

Notes: Ways I Can Improve My Nutritional Habits

_____

_____

_____

_____

_____

_____

_____

_____

_____

_____

"Nothing is impossible, the word itself says,
"I'm possible"

~ Audrey Hepburn

CHAPTER 5

Move With A Purpose

Air is something we can't see, but the average person breaths about 5,000 gallons each day. Without air, we would not be able to survive more than about 9 minutes. It is necessary to stay healthy and staying alive.

Did you know that when the average person breaths a normal breath of air, most of the organs and muscles receive only a minimum amount of that oxygen? In order for all of our organs to achieve an optimal supply of oxygen, we need to move in a manner that will invite more air to be carried to those areas. We need to exercise.

A close look at the human body validates that we were created to move. The three primary anatomical structures (bones, joints, and muscles) work in concert, orchestrating everyday movements we take for granted. Picking up a toddler, walking up and downstairs, and standing up from a chair, all require physical strength that involves the movement of muscles and joints. As long as we are performing these actions with limited problems, we rarely think about the power or forces the human machinery executes to create the action. With age, we begin to lose muscle (particularly around 40-50 years of age), and joints become stiffer. When we lose muscle, we lose strength, and with stiffer joints, we have a diminished range of motion. Both are important health issues that can be avoided or at least slowed with meaningful exercise.

Step #5: Get Regular Exercise to Promote Health and Strength

The best way to get more oxygen distributed to all organs in large supply is through exercise. Exercises like brisk walking, swimming, biking, and hiking are ideal low-impact aerobic exercises that are easy on the joints and demand more oxygen. Additional strength training exercises like push-ups, dips, or squats should be incorporated to provide more muscle strength. The body was made to move, and in most cases, it responds quickly when one gets started with basic exercises. It is not necessary to have any special equipment to get started. With exercise, the circulation of blood is invigorated to move more freely, providing nutrients and oxygen to organs and muscles throughout the body.

We live in a sedentary society, so we must purposefully make sure to get up and exercise if we want to stay healthy. It is easy for most of us to sit too long watching television, surfing the net, driving in a car, working at our desks, etc. Practice breaking that cycle by getting up and moving. Research shows that we are experiencing a serious public health crisis due to inactivity. An article in The Journal of American Medical Association (JAMA) disclosed the detriments of lack of exercise. The article stated that a "high amount of sedentary behavior and low levels of physical activity are associated with increased risk of premature mortality and some chronic diseases."[10] Another article in Time Magazine stated that sitting has been called "the new smoking" because of the wide range of health problems it can trigger. The lack of exercise promotes chronic diseases that result in premature deaths, much like smoking. If physical activity was increased by just 25%, 1.3 million deaths could be prevented.[11]

WOW! Inactivity is DEADLY!

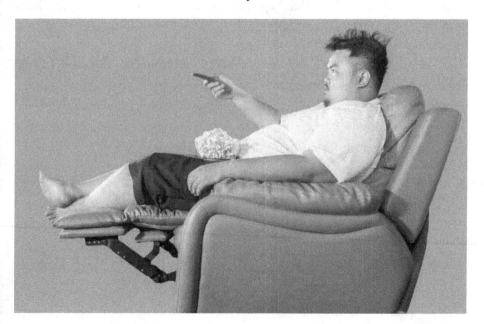

On the other hand, exercise has been proven to increase longevity, build muscle, increase flexibility, lower blood pressure, decrease the risk of diabetes and fight obesity. It is almost like a fountain of youth. Exercise is one of the steps in this program that will not only help negate physical illness but will also help to improve sleep quality, reduce symptoms of depression and assist in managing chronic stress.

If exercise is so good for us and provides so many benefits, why don't .people exercise more?

It takes time and effort to exercise, and for busy people, it often doesn't happen unless it's part of a committed schedule. Exercise must be intentional.

Like eating life-giving food, most people know exercise is good for them, and it is something they should do. Many have good intentions of exercising. However, when the day gets busy, or things run off course, exercise is the one thing that typically falls off the list. Caregivers, busy professionals, and so many others fall prey to these situations.

The American College of Sports Medicine recommends that adults get at least 30 minutes of moderate aerobic exercise (e.g., brisk walking, biking, rebounding) 5 days a week or 20-25 minutes of vigorous exercise (e.g., running, racketball, snow skiing) at least 3 days per week.[12] If one can exercise 45-60 minutes on these days, that is even better.

For those individuals who can't get to the gym on a regular basis or are short on time, even brief bouts of activity at your home or office offer benefits. For instance, if you can't fit in one 30-minute walk during the day, try three ten-minute brisk walks instead. Any activity is better than none. The most important point is to make regular physical activity part of your lifestyle. Commit to moving with a purpose. If you need to improve muscle tone or strength, I recommend trying the exercises included at the end of this chapter. You can track your progress in the "The Real Life Self-Care Journal."

Before starting any exercise program, I encourage you to first check with your health care provider or physician to determine if you can exercise. If the answer is "yes," then don't wait. Schedule exercise as one of the first things on your to-do list, and then "DO IT!"

If you need a fitness trainer to help you develop a safe exercise program and keep you accountable, go to one of my websites:

(www.maydisskeete.issacertifiedtrainer.com or

https://getupandmooove.com) to make contact. I will be happy to assist you in getting on track. You can also check with your local YMCA, recreation center, or commercial gym where trainers are available. A trainer can provide you with an exercise program that is safe, effective, and customized to benefit your health.

No time for a trip to the gym? Try a 30-minute exercise video at home or in the office at

12 Benefits of Exercise

1. Improves cardiorespiratory fitness
2. Lowers risk of stroke and heart disease
3. Helps to lower the risk of high blood pressure
4. Lowers risk of type 2 diabetes
5. Improves bone strength
6. Improves muscular strength and builds lean muscle
7. Improves sleep quality
8. Reduces symptoms of depression
9. Improves digestion and elimination
10. Improves memory and learning abilities
11. Improves joint mobility
12. Helps to strengthen the immune system

Your Gift of Self-love: Get at least 30 minutes of exercise every day; make moving more part of your daily activities

Exercises to Help You Get Started

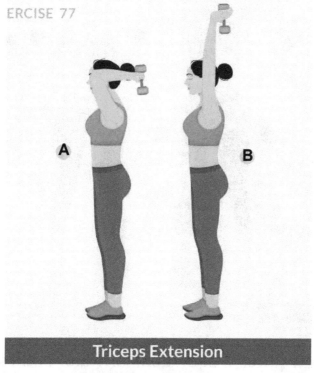

ERCISE 77

A

B

Triceps Extension

Requires 2 dumbbells or water bottles

A. Stand tall with a dumbbell in each hand. Raise arms above the head and bend elbows so that the dumbbells hang behind the head.

B. Extend the elbow to raise the dumbbells up, then repeat. Maintain upright posture throughout the movement.

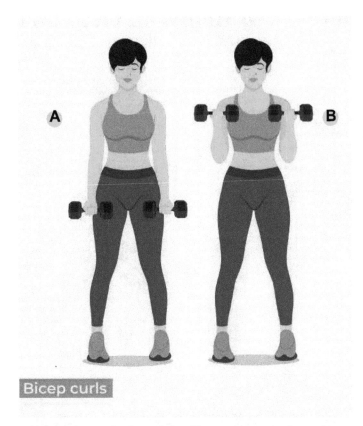

Bicep curls

Requires 2 dumbbells or water bottles

A. Stand tall, holding dumbbells in front of the thigh. The back of the hands should be on the thigh and palms facing away.

B. While holding the dumbbells with a firm grip, flex the elbow to bring the dumbbells up toward the shoulder. Then lower them back to the starting position. Repeat.

Shoulder Press

Requires a dumbbell or water bottle

A. Stand with feet hip-width apart. Bring dumbbells or water bottles up so that the upper arm is parallel to the floor and the palm is facing front. The arm should be in a 90-degree position

B. Press arm up, so that dumbbell/water bottle is over the head. Return arm back to 90-degree position. Repeat

EXERCISE 19

A

B

Jumping Jacks

A. Stand with arms at the side.

B. Jump to bring feet apart and bring hands overhead in an arching motion. Return to starting position, bringing feet back together and hands back to the side. Don't let your knees cave inward while jumping. Land softly by allowing knees to have a slight bend. Continual movement in this fashion provides great aerobic endurance.

Requires a sturdy box, bench, or chair

A. Sit near the edge of a sturdy box, chair, or bench and roll your shoulders slightly back and downward. Place hands under shoulder onto the bench or chair. Place legs outward in front. Move hips off the chair, box, or bench. Bend elbows and lower hips down.

B. Exhale, extend arms, and bring hips up. Repeat.

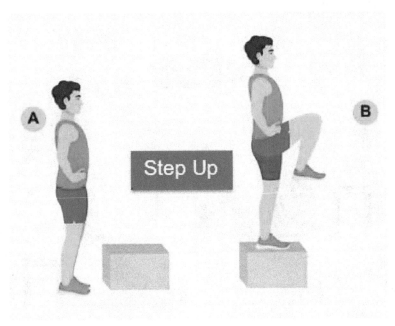

Requires 8" - 12" box or step

A. Stand tall with feet hip-width apart behind a step or box. Keep the body upright (don't lean the chest forward) throughout the movement.

B. Place your entire foot on the step. Use the foot on the step to drive the body up. Raise the other leg and then return it to the floor. Repeat on the other side.

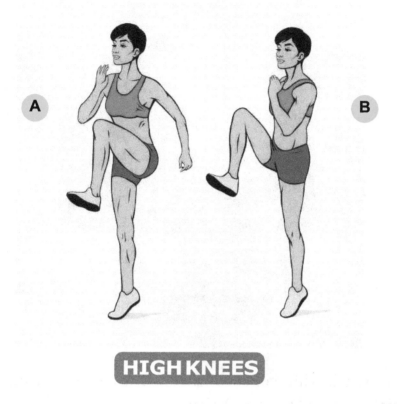

HIGH KNEES

A. Stand tall with arms at the side. Raise one knee toward the chest and propel your arms as if jogging to provide power as you lower the leg.

B. Raise the opposite knee with the same force and continue to alternate movement for several seconds. This is a great warm-up and aerobic conditioning exercise.

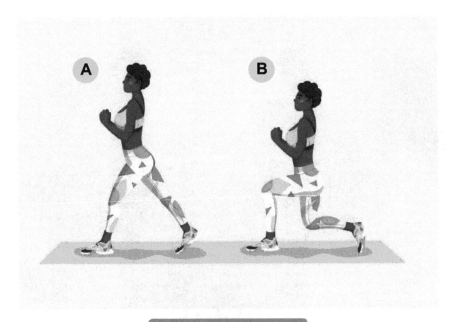

REVERSE LUNGE

A. Stand tall with feet about shoulder-width apart. Keep core tight and slightly lean forward.

B. Step left leg back and drop the knee toward the ground. Keep shoulders rolled back and chest up. Press off the front foot and bring the left leg back to a standing position. Repeat on the opposite side.

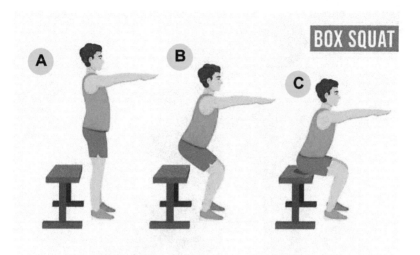

Requires a sturdy box, chair, or bench.

A. Stand with feet about shoulder-width apart or a little wider.

B. Keep chest up and push the buttocks back toward the bench, box, or chair. Knees should bend outward and should track in the same direction as toes. Don't let your knees cave inward.

C. Let buttocks touch the bench, box, or chair, then press through the heels and return to a standing position. Repeat.

A. Stand with feet about shoulder-width apart or a little wider. Keep your chest up and push the buttocks back as if sitting in a chair. Lower body as low as comfortable. Knees should bend outward and track in the same direction as toes. Don't let your knees cave inward.

B. Press through the heels and stand. Repeat.

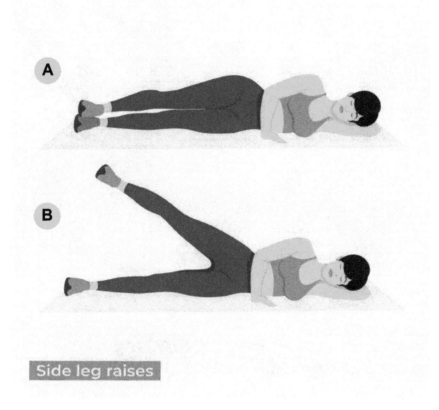

Side leg raises

A. Lie on your side with legs out straight. The lower arm can rest under the head. The top arm can rest on the hip or on the floor.

B. Raise top leg, keeping hips steady and facing forward. Lower leg and repeat several times on this side. Turn over and repeat the other side.

FLUTTER KICKS

A. Lie on your back. Hands should be placed at the side. Push lower back into the floor. Keep legs straight and lift legs up, one at a time (no more than 7- 8 inches). Move the legs up and down like scissors for about 20-30 seconds.

B. Make sure to keep the back to the floor throughout the exercise. Breath throughout the process. Rest and repeat

PUSH UP

A. Start from the ground; chest flat on the floor, place hands next to the chest and toes pressed to the floor.

B. Press through the heel of the hands and raise the torso, chest, and thighs off the ground as one unit. Keep abdominals tight and back straight. Return back to the ground as one unit. Repeat. This exercise can also be done on the knees.

BIRD DOG

A. Lower your body to your hands and knees. Align wrists and elbows under the shoulders.

B. Extend one leg so that the leg is parallel to the floor. At the same time, extend the opposite arm so that it is parallel to the floor. Hold for 3- 5 seconds, then return hand and knee to the floor. Repeat the same process with the other leg and arm.

donkey kicks

A. Start on your hands and knees. Make sure the wrists and elbows are aligned under the shoulders.

B. Pull your core in and continue to breathe; slowly lift one leg and flex the knee. Drive the heel toward the ceiling. Keep your knee at about a 90-degree angle and center your weight so you don't lean to either side. DON'T over arch the back. Lower the knee back to the floor. Repeat

Plank with Leg Lift

A. Lie on the ground, chest down. Place hands next to the chest and press through the heels of the hand, and raise the torso, chest, and thighs off the ground. Keep wrists, elbows and shoulders aligned. Keep feet hip-width apart. Maintain a neutral spine. Keep head neutral; do not press chin into the chest or push chin out.

B. Lift left leg without arching the back. Lower the left leg, then lift the other leg. Maintain a neutral back throughout the process.

SINGLE-LEG GLUTE BRIDGE

A. Lie on your back with feet planted flat on the ground. Place heels of feet about 5-6 inches away from the glutes. Place hands at the side.

B. Engage core and raise hips up. Float one leg up and keep hips parallel to the floor. Squeeze glutes at the top. Lower hips, rest, and repeat.

Mountain Climbers

A. Get into a plank position with wrist, elbows, and shoulders aligned. This can be done from the floor, a bench, or a sturdy chair. Place feet about hip-width apart and keep the core contracted.

B. Draw one knee upward toward the chest without lifting the hips up, release and draw the other knee up toward the chest. Alternate legs as if softly jogging while in this position. A faster pace stimulates aerobic endurance.

Deadbug

A. Lie on your back with your knees bent 90 degrees. The knees will be directly above your hips and your arms extended toward the ceiling. Engage your core and press your lower back into the floor. Keep the back pressed to the floor throughout the entire exercise.

B. Lower one foot toward the floor and extend the opposite arm over the head and toward the floor. Pause and squeeze your abs to raise the leg and arm back to the starting position. Repeat with the other leg and arm. That is one rep.

FULL BODY WORKOUT

If you need an exercise plan to get started, try the full-body circuit outlined in the diagram above. Do this workout 2x-3x per week. It will enhance your strength, mobility, and energy level.

Perform each exercise 12-15 times. Rest 10-15 seconds between exercises, then move to the next exercise.

Repeat the circuit twice. This workout can generally be done in 20 -30 minutes.

Notes: How I Will Move More

_____

_____

_____

_____

_____

_____

_____

_____

_____

_____

"Just Do It!"
~NIKE

CHAPTER 6

Develop Divine Trust and an Attitude of Gratitude

.In this chapter, we will be reviewing the development of spiritual health and practicing an attitude of gratitude as self-care mechanisms. I recognize that there may be many people reading this from other backgrounds and faiths different from Christianity. While I believe everyone can and should choose to believe as their conscience directs, I write this section from a Christian perspective because that is the lifestyle I have embraced and lived throughout my caregiving experience.

I am sure there is someone who is saying, "What does divine trust and gratitude have to do with self-care?" A LOT!

It is all about the thought process. In everything we do, the mindset in which it is approached and tackled has a bearing on the individual. Developing trust and thankfulness are elements that help provide an inward sense of peace in the midst of a storm.

"Finally, brethren, whatever things are true, whatever things are noble, whatever things are just, whatever things are pure, whatever things are lovely, whatever things are of good report, if there is any virtue and if there is anything praiseworthy, meditate on these things." Philippians 4:8 (NKJV)

"Good thoughts and actions can never produce bad results; bad thoughts and actions can never produce good results."
As a Man Thinketh by James Allen, pg. 121

"A merry heart does good like medicine, but a broken spirit dries the bones." Proverbs 17:22 (NKJV)

"Nothing tends more to promote health of body and of soul than does a spirit of gratitude and praise. It is a law of nature that our thoughts and feelings are encouraged and strengthened as we give them utterance... When someone asks how you are feeling, do not try to think of something mournful to tell in order to gain sympathy. Do not talk of your lack of faith and your sorrows and sufferings. Let us talk instead of the great power of God to unite all our interests with His own...Have we not reason to be thankful every moment, thankful even when there are apparent difficulties in our pathway."

The Ministry of Healing by Ellen White, pages 251-254.

Although written over 100 years ago, each of the authors cited in these passages reflects what modern science validates. People who express gratitude and have a divine spiritual relationship experience greater health benefits.

Step #6: Pray and Identify Something to Be Thankful Everyday

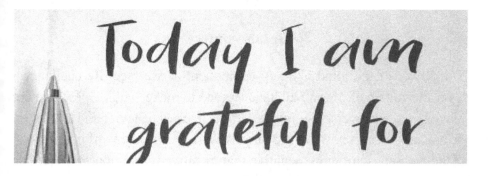

Rarely does a person get through life without some obstacles and disappointments. Sometimes these difficult situations are mixed with shattered dreams and other adversities. How one decides to face these problems can play a huge factor in the mental and physical outcome of the person. Notice I said, 'How one decides to face these problems. Yes, we get to make a choice as to how we will face life challenges.

We can choose to think of challenging situations as learning experiences and look for an opportunity to grow, learn and become better, or we can choose to harbor resentment, anger, and pity. Both thoughts pathways have consequences. Developing the ability to see more good and giving thanks for what we have available aid to provide positive outcomes.

"Be thankful for what you have, you'll end up having more. If you concentrate on what you don't have, you will never ever have enough."

Oprah Winfrey

The power of the mind is a key component as we face life challenges. Over the course of life, we all have learned to make "audiotapes" that are played over and over in our minds. This is learned behavior and may often be associated with how we see ourselves as well as the world around us. If the messages are more negative than positive, it is important that one acknowledges this and makes an effort to change them to more positive messages. This is not always easy, especially if one has been accustomed to thinking dark or negative thoughts or has been conditioned to negativity because of association. If you are prone to depression and somber feelings more than what is considered normal, professional counseling should be sought. A professional counselor can diagnose, advise and assist in achieving mental health that will result in more positive thoughts.

Practicing a shift of your attention from what is painful or negative to more pleasant thoughts helps to cultivate a more positive attitude. Entertaining expressions of gratitude, seeing the good in others, and searching for reasons to be thankful are ways to aid the brain in thinking positive thoughts.

The relationship between the body and mind is a delicate relationship. Both are intimately involved with each other. The type of thoughts entertained as one approaches life situations, including the caregiving experience, has a great bearing on the physical and mental faculties of both the caregiver and those cared for. Pouting, complaining, and whining only promotes more discontent.

What thoughts/messages are you sending to yourself?

Throughout the Bible, there are passages of scripture that speak about trusting God and how demonstrating acts of praise and thanksgiving provide peace and a closer connection with divine power.

"Thou will keep him in perfect peace, whose mind is stayed on thee because he trusts in thee." Isaiah 26:3

"Be not conformed to this world; but be ye transformed by the renewing of your mind, that ye may prove what is that good, and acceptable and perfect, will of God." Romans, 12:2

"And be ye kind one to another, tenderhearted, forgiving one another, even as God for Christ's sake hath forgiven you." Ephesians 4:32

"O give thanks unto the Lord for he is good; for his mercy endureth forever." Psalms 107:1

To write this book, I surveyed a sample of individuals who were currently serving as home caregivers or had been active home caregivers within the last 5 years. 80% of the respondents indicated they felt their spiritual relationship with God gave them strength and peace of mind to deal with the challenges faced.

There appears to be a deep peace that comes when one learns to trust in a Supreme Being that knows all things and has our best interest. Prayer and meditation on Bible verses help many to handle situations in a calmer manner, thereby reducing melancholy and depressing moments. Speaking words of praise and gratitude helps the mind to stay focused on more positive aspects of life. Spending time in nature and reflecting on the grandeur and awesomeness of creation reminds us of a Creator who is in control.

Dan Buettner indicates in his research that people who pay attention to their spiritual health have lower rates of cardiovascular disease, depression, stress, suicide, and their immune systems are more enhanced.[13]

Give yourself the gift of peace and thanksgiving by developing trust in God and expressing gratitude.

(The Resource pages at the end of the book list products that help find/develop Spiritual trust.)

Ways to develop divine trust and gratitude

Pray daily.
Read and meditate on a Bible scripture every day.
Connect with a like-minded community to fellowship.
Give personal praise and thanks to God regardless of the circumstance.
Write 5 things you are thankful for every day.
Listen/sing cheerful songs.

Your Gift of Self-love: Practice thinking positive thoughts daily; look for the good in others; develop a relationship with God.

Notes: How I Will Engage Positive Thinking

CHAPTER 7

Make Time for Rest and Recreation

Many Americans have difficulty balancing work and their personal life. We don't think twice about scheduling a business meeting into our already busy day or working through lunch so we can accommodate a potential client. However, we have a difficult time including downtime or recreation for ourselves and with our family.

Taking time to refresh and rejuvenate is a special gift everyone should give to themselves. This may seem difficult at first, but when one recognizes the importance and begins to include time to refresh and rejuvenate, it becomes easier to deal with being a caregiver.

Step #7: Schedule Time to Rest And Relax

Dan Buettner cites in his book "The Blue Zones" that long-living Seventh-Day Adventists help keep a healthy balance in their busy lives by devoting one whole day, a 24–hour period, to refresh and rejuvenate.[14] They observe what is called the Sabbath as mentioned throughout the Bible (Genesis 2:2-3, Exodus 20:8-11, and Mark 2:27,28).

This group of Christians reserves the time from Friday sundown to Saturday sundown to spend with their families and friends, serving the community and seeking spiritual and physical rejuvenation. During this time, they generally do not go to work or participate in business activities. They allow themselves this time to be free from the daily stresses of life.[15]

To this group, the Sabbath is observed as a special day to reflect on the Creator and relax with family and friends. There is something everyone can learn from this practice. In following God's Biblical law, these Christians not only gain special spiritual time with God but also enjoy a more balanced life, relaxation time, and a longer life span.

Ways to incorporate recreation and rest into a busy schedule is by planning special days to be free from daily stress. Designate a weekend each month to pursue a personal interest. Here are some examples that may interest you. Schedule a date weekend with your spouse, and volunteer with an organization you like (e.g., Habitat for Humanity, Humane Society).

Go camping, run or walk a 5K, get a massage, find a cozy spot alone and curl up with a book, enjoy a hobby or go to the beach to enjoy a sunset. I think you get the picture.

Periodically, it is important to take a longer break from the routine and do something that will help you to regroup/recreate and think about other things outside of the daily routine. Doing something new stimulates the neurons in the brain and generates new pathways. You will be amazed at how taking a rest period from a regular routine provides enjoyment and adds refreshment to the mind and body. You will return able to perform your responsibilities more effectively and be a better companion and caregiver to those you serve.

Playing outside with your kids, going on a picnic, and making memories with people that matter is most important. These things are all possible, and it helps to promote good health.

The important point in this chapter is to recognize that you can and should add value to your life and those who mean most by creating enjoyable moments, exploring new things, and taking time for relaxation and fellowship. Schedule time for rest and restoration in your "The Real Life Self-Care Journal," and make sure to follow through.

Relaxation and Recreation Moments to Consider:

1. Set aside one day each week for relaxation, rest, and fellowship.

2. Reserve a special day or a weekend once a month just for your interest.

3. Schedule and go on a vacation for rest and relaxation at least once a year.

4. Volunteer at an organization that you believe in.

5. Take up a hobby or project you've wanted to try (e.g., Painting, crafts, etc.)

Your Gift of Self-love: Set aside one day each week to do no work, to relax, and to fellowship.

Notes: How I Will Create Time for Rest and Recreation

_____

_____

_____

_____

_____

_____

_____

_____

_____

_____

"Don't count the days, make the days count." ~ Muhammad Ali

FINAL THOUGHT

My caregiving experience ended 3 months prior to me starting this book. My mother passed from natural causes in 2020 during the height of the COVID-19 pandemic. She died peacefully in her sleep at 91 years of age.

As I reflect on my experience in caring for her, there are many lessons I learned and appreciated. First, I can unequivocally say that I am grateful I had the opportunity to care for my mother. It was a blessing to provide that gift of love to one who had done so much for me. It was hard work, often tiring, but there were cheerful moments that I will always treasure. I learned a lot about myself and appreciated the wisdom gained during that time. Without that experience, I would not have written this book.

Second, this experience gave me a front view of the challenges and obstacles caregivers encounter. I have greater respect for caregivers and honor their commitment and passion for helping others. Whether it is a child, spouse, parent, or someone else, the gift of caregiving is unmatched love.

Third, without this experience, I may not have recognized I was developing unhealthy habits that were contributors to a serious health concern.

Last, writing this book revealed to me that the problems many caregivers encounter are not solely associated with the challenges of caregiving, although that is a true challenge, but are more related to the mindset presented by the caregiver when approaching each issue.

As you navigate the journey of self-care, I encourage everyone to embrace developing a healthy approach to all of life's situations and practice the 7- step approach outlined in this reading.

RESOURCES

Chapter 1 – "HELP! I've Fallen and Can't Get Up"

Recommended Sources to assist caregivers of adults:

I. STATE AGENCIES AND RESPITE CARE RESOURCES
It's usually best to begin looking for local respite care resources through your local Area Agency on Aging.

Area Agencies on Aging
Eldercare Locator
927 15th NW, 6th Floor
Washington, DC 20005
Eldercare Locator: 800-677-1116
www.eldercare.acl.gov

The National Respite Network and Resource Center also may offer respite care funding and support by state. To find state-based resources, visit the website for the **U.S. Department of Health and Human Services Aging Resources at HHS.gov.**

You may also find resources in your state by visiting the website of Access to Respite Care and Help (ARCH) National Respite Network and Resource Center at archrespite.gov.

II. VOLUNTEER ORGANIZATIONS

Many people love to work with seniors by volunteering through local and national organizations. Here are a few organizations that can provide a helping hand.

National organizations with respite care volunteers

Elder Helpers: Elder Helpers recruits, screens, and trains volunteers to provide respite care and other assistance for seniors. You can also contact them and request a volunteer to help you. The website for this organization is **elderhelpers.org.**

AmeriCorps Senior: Volunteers with AmeriCorps Senior give back in several ways. Many serve as a friend or companions by providing friendship and assistance to seniors who have difficulty with daily living tasks. Volunteers are trained by the organization and assist older adults so they can remain independent longer. They also provide respite to family caregivers. The website for this organization is americorps.gov, and the national service hotline is (800) 942-2677.

Religious-based volunteers

Additional sources for community volunteers may include churches, mosques, synagogues, and other faith-based groups. Check with your congregation or those in your area.

You may also explore faith-based religious senior care volunteer services through

The Senior Living Organization
www.seniorliving.org.

Other faith-based organizations that provide senior care include:

**Catholic Charities Senior and Caregiver Support
ccseniorservices.org**

**Help for the Elderly: Christian Aid Ministries
christianaidministries.org**

**In Home Senior Care: Christian Senior Care Network
christianseniorcarenetwork.com**

III. GOVERNMENT BENEFITS

Medicare covers respite care for hospice patients. Additionally, Veterans can obtain financial assistance from the VA for respite care.

If you're a caregiver for a loved one receiving hospice care through Medicare Part A (Hospital Insurance), Medicare will pay for short-term inpatient respite care in a Medicare-approved facility such as a hospice facility, hospital, or skilled nursing residence.

Typically, you can get respite care more than once for up to five days at a time — but only on an "occasional basis." Refer to Medicare's website.

Veteran Affairs Respite Care Benefit

Military veterans may be eligible for Veterans Administration (VA) respite care, which can assist families with short-term care. The following government agencies may be helpful in providing more information regarding VA and Medicare benefits.

Department of Veterans Affairs (VA)
810 Vermont Ave. NW
Washington, DC 20420
(800) 827-1000
www.va.gov

Paralyzed Veterans of America (PVA)
Veterans Benefits Department
801 18th St., NW
Washington, DC 20006
(800) 424-8200
www.pva.org

Centers for Medicare & Medicaid Services (CMS)
Richard Bolling Federal Bldg, Room 235
601 East 12th Street
Kansas City, MO 64106
(800) MEDICARE
www.medicare.gov

IV. HOME CARE AND ADULT DAY CARE

Additional sources that provide assistance with daycare and help in the home are available in most areas. The following list are resources that may be helpful in locating support in your area.

National Adult Day Services Association, Inc.
8201 Greensboro Drive, Suite 300
McLean, Virginia 22102
(866)-890-7357 or (703) 610-9035
info@nadsa.org www.nadsa.org

National Association for Home Care
228 7th Street, SE Washington, DC 20003
(202) 547-7424
www.nahc.org

Meals on Wheels Association of America
www.momaa.org

ABLEDATA - Assistive Devices
8630 Fenton Street, Ste 930
Silver Springs, MD 20910
(800) 227-0216
TTY: (301) 608-8912
www.abledata.com

V. ADDITIONAL CAREGIVER RESOURCES

There are several other resources available to caregivers and families who are trying to navigate caring for adults. This includes insurance sources for long-term care, legal assistance, and more. The following listings are some sources that have been found helpful.

Long Term Care Insurance/Health Insurance

National Association of Insurance Commissioners - NAIC
Hall of States
444 North Capitol Street, NW Suite 701
Washington, DC 20001
(202) 624-7790
www.naic.org

American Association of Health Plans
601 Pennsylvania Avenue NW
South Building
Washington, DC 20004 www.ahip.org

American Association of Long-Term Care Insurance
3835 E. Thousand Oaks Blvd. Suite 336
Westlake Village, CA 91362
(818) 597-3227
www.aaltci.org

The Center for Long-Term Care Reform
2212 Queen Anne Ave. North #110
Seattle, WA 98109
(206) 283-7036
www.centerltc.org

Legal Resources

National Academy of Elder Law Attorneys
1604 N. Country Club Road
Tucson, AZ 85716
www.naela.org

Commission on Legal Problems of the Elderly
www.abanet.org/elderly

Senior Law
www.seniorlaw.com

Caregiver Support Organizations

Caregiver Action Network
1130 Connecticut Avenue, NW
Washington, DC 20036
(202) 454-3970
www.caregiveraction.org

Well Spouse Foundation
63 West Main Street - Suite H
Freehold, NJ 07728
(800) 838-0879
www.wellspouse.org

Senior Advocacy and Interest Groups

National Consumers League
1701 K Street, NW, Ste. 1200
Washington, DC 20006
(202) 835-3323
www.natlconsumersleague.org

Families USA
www.familiesusa.org

ElderWeb
www.elderweb.com

United Seniors Health Council - USHC
409 3rd St., SW, Ste. 200
Washington, DC 20024
(202) 479-6673
www.unitedseniorshealth.org

American Health Care Association
1201 L Street, NW
Washington DC 20005
(202) 842-4444
www.ahca.org

Alliance for Retired Americans
888 16th St., NW
Washington, DC 20006
(888) 373-6497
www.retiredamericans.org

American Society on Aging - ASA
833 Market Street
Suite 511
San Francisco, CA 94103
(415) 974-9600
www.asaging.org info@asaging.org

AARP
www.aarp.org

Benefits Check-Up
www.benefitscheckup.org

Alliance for Aging Research
2021 K Street, NW Suite 305
Washington, DC 20006
(800) 639-2421
www.agingresearch.org
info@agingresearch.org

Resources for Housing

The Assisted Living Federation of America
11200 Waples Mill Rd.
Suite 150
Fairfax, VA 22030
(703) 691-8100
www.alfa.org info@alfa.org

National Shared Housing Resource Center
www.nationalsharedhousing.org

National Center for Assisted Living
1201 L Street, NW
Washington, DC 20003
(202) 842-444
www.ncal.org

Leading Age
2519 Connecticut Ave. NW
Washington, DC 20008
(800) 508-9442
www.leadingage.org

The Eden Alternative
www.edenalt.com

Resources for Hospice Care

Partnership For Caring
1620 Eye Street NW Suite 202
Washington, DC 20006
(202) 296-8071
www.caringinfo.org

Hospice Foundation of America
2001 S. St. NW #300
Washington, DC 20009
(800) 854-3402
www.hospicefoundation.org

National Hospice & Palliative Care Organization
1700 Diagonal Road
Suite 625
Alexandria, VA 22314
(703) 837-1500
www.nhpco.org

Resourceful Podcasts

Daughterhood, The Podcast

A resources podcast for primary caregivers. Features experts guest such as doctors, legislators, and researchers. Provide helpful tips and information.

Fading Memories

This podcast is for those caring for an adult with dementia. Understanding dementia, prevention techniques, and practical advice for caregivers are presented.

The Senior Caregiver Podcast

Podcast airs monthly to talk about the joys and challenges of senior caregiving. Get information about how to care for aging loved ones and yourself.

Chapter 3 - Get More Sleep

The National Institute of Health (NIH) provides a free booklet entitled "Your Guide to Healthy Sleep." You can download a copy from www.nih.gov or write and request a booklet.

National Institute of Health
9000 Rockville Pike
Bethesda, MD 20892

Other helpful websites and books that provide helpful tips on improving sleep include:

National Sleep Foundation
www.sleepfoundation.org

American Academy of Sleep Medicine
www.aasmnet.org

"The Sleep Revolution: Transforming Your Life, One Night at a Time"
by Arianna Huffington

"Sleep Smarter: 21 Essential Strategies to Sleep Your Way to Better
Body, Better Health and Bigger" by Shawn Stevenson

Individuals who experience ongoing sleep deprivation issues (sleep apnea, insomnia, sleepwalking, etc.) should contact their physician and let him/her know about the problem.

Chapter 4 - Choose Life-Giving Nutrients

You can retrieve a copy of the Healthy Eating Plate nutritional diagram on page 23 by going to the website **www.hsph.harvard.edu/nutritionsource** and download.

The Real Life Self-Care Journal is not only a journal but also provides helpful nutritional information and meal planning tips to assist with time management and self-care tracking.

The Real Life Self-Care Journal by Maydis Skeete

Chapter 5 - Move With Purpose

Below are websites to organizations that provide individuals with information to help get started in an exercise program or assist with training and accountability to stick with regular exercise.

https://getupandmooove.com
www.mayoclinic.org
ymca.org

Chapter 6 – Develop Divine Trust and an Attitude of Gratitude

Helpful Resources for Divine Intervention

Amazing Facts is a Christian Media company that provides Christian media productions, Bible studies, and Free products.

Amazing Facts
www.amazingfacts.org

Breath of Life Ministries is a television ministry that seeks to help individuals discover God's life-enabling concern for their well being.

Breath of Life Ministries
https://breathoflife.tv

Holy Bible
www.holybible.com

The It Is Written Bible Study Guides are the perfect way to learn God's plan for your life! These free lessons guide you step-by-step into a deeper understanding of scripture.

It Is Written
www.itiswritten.com

Power of the Lamb Ministries provides sermons, Bible studies, counseling, and special teaching on how to study the Bible.

Power of the Lamb Ministries
www.powerofthelamb.com

Resourceful Books

The following books provide impactful exercises on how to recognize abundance, no matter the moment, and provide help in developing the positive psychology of gratefulness to cultivate a healthier and happy life.

"The Gratitude Project: How the Science of Thankfulness Can Reverse Our Brains for Resilence, Optimism and the Greater Good" by Jeremy Adam Smith

"Wake Up Grateful" by Kristi Nelson

Everyday Gratitude: Inspiration for Living Life as a Gift" by Brother David Steindl-Rast

The Life-Changing Power of Gratitude by Marc Reklau

Resourceful Podcast or Video

Wake Up with Gratitude

This podcast is found on Amazon Music. It explores ways to practice gratitude when faced with challenges.

5 Ways to Show Gratitude
by Brian Tracy (YouTube)

The Power of Gratitude
Oprah Winfrey Speech
By Motivational Instinct (YouTube)

PRAYERS, QUOTES, AND TIPS

A Caregivers Prayer

Dear Father,

Today I come asking for a fresh wind of grace from You. Lead me and guide me in the role of caregiver.

Let me gather strength from You hour by hour. Let me graciously take assistance from others when they offer it. Grant me wisdom for any new issues I may face today.

Remind me when I need a break so I can take care of myself as well. May I remember to be grateful and thankful for all the blessings you provide.

Guide my thoughts, words, and actions. Help me to find the blessings and lessons in every situation. Remind me to think about things that are lovely and good. Place a song in my heart and laughter in mouth as I care for my love one each day. Show me how to walk this path with peace, love, and joy. Amen

"Doctors diagnose, nurses heal and the caregivers make sense of it all."

~Brett H. Lewis

Keep Calm
Caregiving is
NOT for wimps

The KeepcalmStudio.com

To do what no one else will do
a way no one else can do
in spite of all we go through
~that is a Caregiver

I know the plans I have for you and they are good.

Jeremiah 29:11

"Remember in the long run you will benefit from caregiving because you will have no regrets knowing that you did what you could and what was right."

~Gail L

A Prayer for Caregivers

May God gift you with

Balm for your heart

Peace for your mind

Strength for each challenge

Courage to hope

Grace for each moment

Rest for each day

Faith to trust

In God's loving way. Amen

To order additional copies of

Self-Care for the Caregiver

A guilt-free way to love yourself while caring for others

or

The Real Life Self-Care Journal

Send a request to mail: guiltfreeselfcare@gmail.com

Or order from various bookstores and markets

If you are interested or need assistance with an exercise program that is customized to meet your busy schedule, contact Maydis Skeete at getupandmooove@gmail.com.

You may also go to
https://getupandmooove.com or
https://www.maydisskeete.issacertifiedtrainer.com for more information.

END NOTES

[1]Mariotti, A. Future Science OA, 2015 November 1(3), "The Effects of Chronic Stress on Health New Insights into the Molecular Mechanism of Brain-body Communication."

[2]Becher, J. Forbes Business, August 12, 2015, Forbes, "6 Quotes To Help You Understand Why It's Important to Say No."

[3]Jones, J. Gallup News, Wellbeing, December 19, 2013, "In US, 40% Get Less Than Recommended Amount of Sleep."

[4]Preidt, R. WebMD Archives-Healthline, August 8, 2016, "Drowsy Driving Causes 1 in 5 Fatal Crashes: Report."

[5]National Sleep Foundation, Sleep in America Poll 2018, "Sleep and Effectiveness are Linked but Few Plan Their Sleep."

[6]Kroese, DeRiddens, Evers, Adriaennse, Frontiers of Psychology, June 19, 2014.

[7]Genesis 1:29, King James Bible.

[8]Buettner, Dan, "The Secrets of Living Longer," National Geographic November 2005, 2-27.

[9]Weil, A. MD, "Dr. Weil's Daily Tip, Inflammation," October 27, 2011.

[10]Journal of American Medical Association, "Joint Prevalence of Sitting Time and Leisure- US Adults,2015- 2016," November 20, 2019, Vol.320. No.19.

[11]Time Magazine, "Most Americans Sit Way Too Much, According to CDC," November 20, 2018.

[12]ACSM's Resources for the Personal Trainer, 5th edition, pg 415.

[13]Buettner, D. The Blue Zones, page 288.

[14]ibid.

[15]Buettner, D., The Blue Zones, pg 148-150

CPSIA information can be obtained
at www.ICGtesting.com
Printed in the USA
LVHW080837231222
735844LV00019B/142